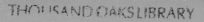

# one woolly wombat

Written by Rod Trinca and Kerry Argent

Illustrated by Kerry Argent

A CRANKY NELL BOOK

Kane/Miller Book Publishers
Brooklyn, New York & La Jolla, California

## OTHER BOOKS FROM KANE/MILLER

The Magic Bubble Trip

The House From Morning to Night

Wilfrid Gordon McDonald Partridge

Brush

I Want My Potty

Girl From the Snow Country

Cat In Search of a Friend

The Truffle Hunter

Goodbye Rune

Winnie the Witch

The Umbrella Thief

The Park Bench

Sorry, Miss Folio!

Paul and Sebastian

The Night of the Stars

First American Edition 1985 by Kane/Miller Book Publishers
Brooklyn, New York & La Jolla, California

Originally published in Australia by Omnibus Books in 1982
Copyright © 1982 Kerry Argent. All rights reserved.
For information contact: Kane/Miller Book Publishers,
P.O. Box 529, Brooklyn, New York 11231

Library of Congress Cataloging in Publication Data

Trinca, Rod.
  One woolly wombat.

  "A Cranky Nell book."
  Summary: Humorous illustrations depict fourteen
Australian animals, introduced in rhyme, along with
the numbers from one to fourteen.
  1. Children's stories, Australian. [1. Zoology—
Australia—Fiction. 2.  Australia—Fiction.
3. Counting. 4. Stories in rhyme] I.  Argent, Kerry,
1960- ill. II. Title.
PX8.3.T6950n 1985   [E]   84-21854
ISBN 0-916291-00-6

Printed and bound in Singapore by Tien Wah Press Pte Ltd

5   6   7   8   9   10

# one woolly wombat

one woolly wombat sunning by the sea

two cuddly koalas sipping gumnut tea

three warbling magpies waking up the sun

four thumping kangaroos dancing just for fun

five pesky platypuses splashing with their feet

six cheeky possums looking for a treat

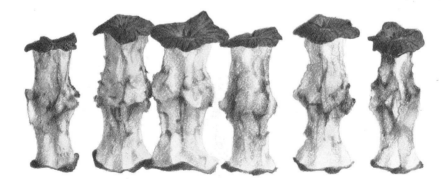

seven emus running . . . in and out the bush

eight spiky echidnas eating ants — whoosh

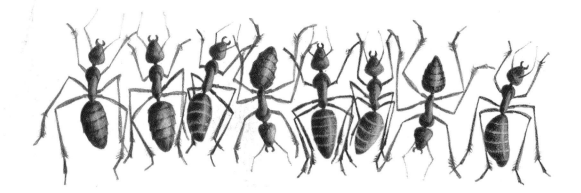

nine hungry goannas wondering what to cook

ten giggly kookaburras writing riddle books

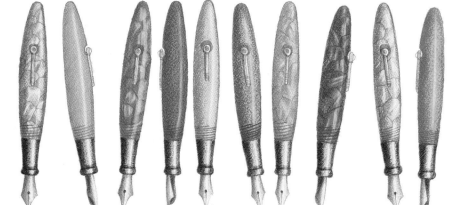

eleven dizzy dingoes twirling with their paws

twelve crazy cockatoos counting on their claws

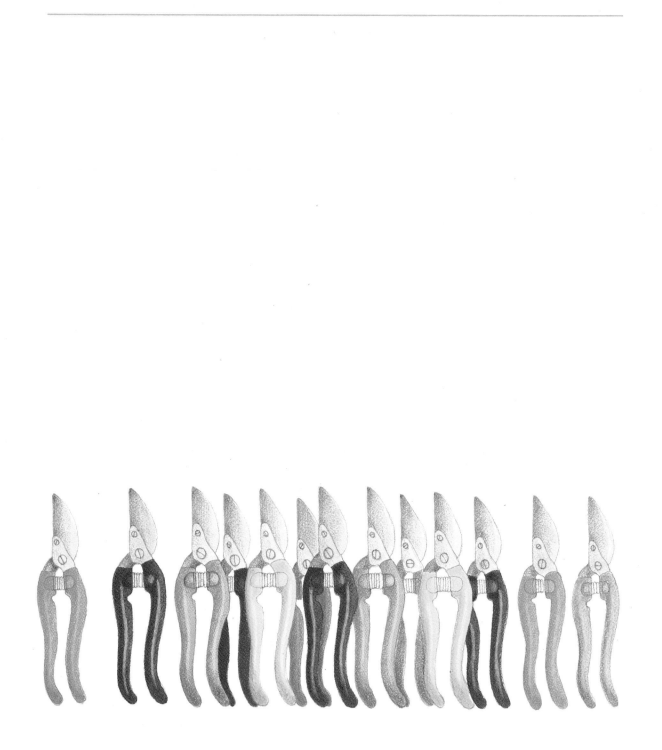

fourteen slick seals sailing out to sea

one woolly wombat sunning by the sea
two cuddly koalas sipping gumnut tea
three warbling magpies waking up the sun
four thumping kangaroos dancing just for fun
five pesky platypuses splashing with their feet
six cheeky possums looking for a treat
seven emus running . . . in and out the bush
eight spiky echidnas eating ants — whoosh
nine hungry goannas wondering what to cook
ten giggly kookaburras writing riddle books
eleven dizzy dingoes twirling with their paws
twelve crazy cockatoos counting on their claws
thirteen hopping mice picking desert pea
fourteen slick seals sailing out to sea